G000146784

NEVER SEEN THE SEA

A novelette

HOLLY WATSON

OPEN PEN

First Published in 2020
by Open Pen, 25 Crescent Road, London, E13 0LU

openpen.co.uk

9781916413665

OPNOV006

OPEN PEN NOVELETTES #5
"Never Seen The Sea"
First Edition
© Holly Watson
Cover illustration by Pierre Buttin - pierrebuttin.com
© Pierre Buttin

A large amount of this book first published as standlone pieces on the author's website, The Coventry Conch.

Printed by Clays.

LADIES NIGHT

7.35pm

The doorbell rings, and Nanny Pam leaves the kitchen to answer it. When she comes back she says, *Ladies, say hello to Mystic Mickey!*

He says, *Now then, ladies, who's ready to talk to the other side? When I say, 'Are you ready to let the spirits enter?', you all need to say, 'Yes Mickey!' So, are you ready to let the spirits enter?*

We are all ready so we say, *Yes, Mickey!*

7pm

Me and my sister Jenny have been dropped off round Nanny Pam's house because Mum and Dad have gone to see Uncle Steve's band Spaghetti Function play.

Mum wasn't sure about letting us go to Nanny Pam's tonight, because she's having one of her ladies' nights. I heard Nanny Pam tell her it would be OK though, because Dirty Dean's put his back out, so won't be able to perform tonight.

When we get to Nanny Pam's, Auntie Maeve answers the door. Auntie Maeve isn't my real auntie, but she does work with Nanny Pam on the fag counter in Tesco. I like her; she tells funny stories, like once she told us that her sister had collected all the hair from her Alsatian out of the carpet for three years, and then made a jumper out of it. Another time she said an elephant nicked a Wagon Wheel out of her handbag at West Midlands Safari Park.

A few more of Nanny Pam's friends from the fag counter, plus a few neighbours, are sat in her living room. Nanny Pam is showing them her new dimmer switch by clicking the light off, and then turning it back on again really slowly.

Auntie Maeve gets a fag out of her bag and lights it up with a lighter that has a photo of a man wearing nothing apart from a sombrero on it. Nanny Pam asks Maeve, *What the hell are you smoking? They bloody stink!* Auntie Maeve says she's had a bit of a cold, so she's smoking menthols.

I'm not sure I like ladies night so far. A cheesy looking lady called Lisa, who smells like the sniffy bits in the Avon catalogue, is trying to sell some Tupperware boxes. Nanny Pam's friends keep asking her really stupid questions about whether or not they can put them in the oven.

After everyone fills out plastic box order forms, we move into the kitchen. Nanny Pam has put on a buffet. All the food is brown, apart from the ham, which is grey.

Cheesy Lisa asks what the triangle things on the silver platter are. Nanny Pam tells her that they are *SAM-MO-SAS*. Lisa nibbles one and starts fanning her mouth. *I'm sorry, Pam,* she says, *but they're way too spicy for me. I'm not a great lover of Chinese food.*

Maeve makes a joke about the little wrinkly sausages and her husband. Everyone laughs. I look at Jenny and she was laughing too. I know she's faking though. She's going really over the top and pretending to wipe away tears from her eyes.

7.40pm
Nanny Pam dims the light, and me and Jenny sit really close to each other on the pouf.

Mickey starts by asking his spirit guide, Derek, to help him. He says that Derek lives on the other side and can go and fetch people we want to speak to.

Are you there, Derek? Derek, are you there?

Jenny grabs my hand when Mickey starts speaking in a strangled high voice, *I'm here Mickey, and I have someone with me. He wants to say that he's having a cuppa and he's happy now.*

Nanny Pam's neighbour Maureen says it sounds like her husband, Ray.

Mickey says in his normal voice, *Derek, do we have Ray with us?* Then, he says in his weird voice, *It is Ray and he wants to say that he's OK and he's remembering a holiday that they had somewhere hot. Was it Spain... Portugal... Greece?*

Maureen starts crying and says, *Wales... he's talking about our holiday in Wales.*

Yes, that's right, Wales! Anyway, Ray wants you to know the dinners are alright up here, but they're not as nice as yours. He's got to go now, though. His favourite program is about to start on the telly.

But he only really liked the snooker, and that's not on for another month...

Yeah, Derek's saying something about the schedules are different up there love.

8pm
After Cheesy Lisa has spoken to her Great Auntie on the other side and Auntie Maeve has spoken to her dead Border Terrier, Mystic Mickey starts going on about Derek being tired and needing to pack it in for the evening.

Everyone goes back into the kitchen for a drink. Jenny and me watch Mystic Mickey sniff a samosa and eat six vol-au-vents, while Maureen asks him all about Ray and whether he's met another woman on the other side.

9pm

When everyone's gone, me, Jenny, and Nanny Pam snuggle up on the sofa. I ask Nanny Pam if she was sad that she didn't get to speak to anyone. Nanny Pam says she's not arsed, everything Mickey says is a load of shit. It's never hot in Wales.

Nanny Pam promises that when she dies she'll come back and haunt us herself, so we don't have to waste forty quid on Mystic Mickey.

THE LIE

10am

It's Harvest Festival at school. Usually I like Harvest Festival because we have a massive assembly, which means we don't have to do any work for a whole morning, and instead have to sing songs about food and Jesus.

Every year for Harvest Festival, Mrs. Boyle, the school receptionist, asks us to bring food in for the poor people. Before she takes it to the church, she makes a massive display in the assembly hall so everyone can see how much food we've got. Everyone's pointing out what they've brought in, if I was in a better mood I'd look in the display for the out of date tin of beans and sausages Nanny Pam gave me to hand in, but I'm too busy worrying.

Yesterday I told a really big lie.

YESTERDAY

12.30pm

Some people from my class are sat on the climbing frame in the playground talking about stuff. I'm stood underneath, by the slide with my cousin Amy listening to them all, looking at Tom. The Nike tick Tom had shaved into his head is starting to grow out and I've started to fancy him again.

Tom says that his mum saw Jet and Wolf from Gladiators in town on Saturday opening a new Safeway. Sammy tells Tom how she went to see Gladiators with her auntie and that she saw Shadow outside afterwards. I feel weird watching Sammy talk to Tom, my tummy starts to turn, and before I can think, I start telling Tom and everyone else the lie.

I was at Safeway on Saturday with my nan, because she wanted to try a frothy coffee in the new cafe, and I met Jet.

Everyone looks down from the climbing frame at me. Sammy starts laughing and says, *Yeah right, chinny chin chin.* Amy is staring at me, she knows I was at her house watching TV all weekend, but I stare her out, and tell her to shut her face with my eyes. I feel really hot and know I've gone red but I can't stop lying.

I did meet her, ask my Dad... I got her autograph.

Sammy says, *Bring it in tomorrow then!*

I tell her I will, then speed walk to the toilets clenching my bum cheeks together, because like usual when I'm nervous, I feel like there's going to be a poocano. Luckily, it's a false alarm, but I lock myself in a loo and start crying anyway.

Amy knocks on the door. She says, *Are you OK, Hol? What are you going to do?'*

I tell her that I don't know, and that I think I'm going to have to move school, which makes Amy cry too..

3.30pm
I run out of my classroom even faster than usual and grab my little brother Josh, who is in the little school cloakroom trying to do his zip up. I yank his coat shut and make him run up to Dad who's waiting in the playground for us. I whisper to Dad, Don't say anything to anyone, we need to get to the car and go home, now!

3.40pm
In the car on the way home, I tell Dad all about the lie and start crying again. I ask him if we can drive to the National Indoor Arena in Birmingham where they make Gladiators and try to meet Jet.

Dad says he's got a better plan.

5.00pm
I don't eat any dinner, even though it's my favourite, Findus Crispy Pancakes. I'm too nervous about Dad's plan.

I go and get my special box in mine and Jenny's room, inside there's an autograph book that Nanny Pam bought me last year. She got it for when we went to meet Shefali, the weather girl from Midlands Today, at West Orchards Shopping Centre last year. So far it only has Shefali's signature in, but it's about to have Jet's.

Dad practices what he thinks Jet's signature might be for a bit and I write what I think Dad should put in the book, on a scrap piece of paper:

Dear Holly,

It was really cool meeting you in Safeway on Saturday. When you're eighteen you can definitely be a Gladiator with Wolf and me! I'll speak to John Anderson and see if we can get you in soon for a VIP tour and a go on the Travelator.

Friends Forever,
Jet xxxxxxxxxxxxxxxxxxxxxxxxxxxxxxxxxxxxxxxxxxxxxxxxxxxxxxxxxxxxxxx

6.00pm
Dad says that it will look more real if we just write 'To Holly, Love Jet', because she wouldn't have time to write a lot.

Dad does big girly writing, draws a smiley face inside the o in love and does a big X at the end.

TODAY

11am

When we walk out of assembly I spot the beans and sausages on the display table next to a bottle of Tango Orange and a box of Mint Matchmakers, I think about someone skint having all that for dinner and it makes me feel a bit better.

I sneak back to my classroom and keep my head down looking at the green tag on my Kickers, when I get to my table, I can feel everyone looking at me. Sammy walks over. *You got it?*

I pull out my autograph book and can feel my hands shaking. Tom comes over with Kevin to have a look as well.

I open the first page and Tom asks, *Who's signature's that?* I tell him it's Shefali's and say that I met her at West Orchards last year.

You met Shefali! No way! What was she like?

Sammy keeps her trap shut for once, while I tell Tom all about how me and Nanny Pam met Shefali, and how nice she is, and that she told us what the weather was going to be like for the next few days, before she'd even said it on the news. Then I show him Jet's signature but he's not really that arsed about it.

Sammy sulks back to her table, while I chat to Tom about

the time he thought he saw Ryan Giggs but it turned out it wasn't actually him, just someone who looked a bit like him from behind. It's a dead boring story but I just switch off and think about whether Shefali would come to our wedding if we invited her.

NEVER SEEN THE SEA

2pm

My teacher Mrs. Woods has sent Alan out of the class for calling her an arsehole.

2.05pm

When you get sent out of class you're meant to wait outside and face the wall, but when Mrs. Woods goes to tell Alan to come back in, he's gone.

I don't know why Mrs. Woods bothers sending Alan out any more, he just legs it.

2.10pm

Mrs. Woods tells me to go and look for Alan, because I'm one of the only people he talks to when he's got one on him.

People don't really like Alan. He gets quite angry about things, and Natalie said that his mum came into school with a knife once. I don't mind him though; he hates school even more than I do. And he does funny things like eating pages from his workbook and saying they taste like prawn cocktail crisps.

2.15pm

I look in all the usual spots for Alan. Last time he was in the craft cupboard sticking glitter and googly eyes to his school jumper.

This time he's lying on the school field with his top off and his hands behind his head. I walk up to him and ask, *Are you coming in, Alan?*

He tells me to piss off, but I sit down next to him anyway.

He says, *I'm trying to get a suntan.*

I tell him that I got a tan last year on holiday in Majorca, and that I'm not sure you can get one in Coventry, in February.

He tells me that he's never been on holiday, not even in England. He's never seen the sea.

2.20pm
I lie down next to Alan; we close our eyes and pretend we're on a holiday. I tell him the beach is like the sandpit in the infants' playground, but much bigger and with less cat shit in it.

He says that he wants to go to the Caribbean, because he saw Mr. Motivator exercising on a beach there on GMTV, and he had a Bounty at his nan's once.

2.25pm
I tell Alan that we should go back inside. He stands up and puts his jumper back on. It's covered in red glitter and googly eyes.

We walk back to our classroom together.

THE CAR BOOT

6am

Me and Nanny Pam are loading her car full of stuff for a boot sale we're doing at the Unicorn Club car park this morning. I ask where all of the stuff came from, and Nanny Pam says, *It's the last lot of your Grandad's dodgy old crap.*

8am

The car is so full of stuff that I have to sit where people's feet usually are.

Nanny Pam has to tell me to duck whenever she thinks she sees a policeman.

I'm sat next to a Roses tin full of PG Tips Chimpanzee cards. I tell Nanny Pam they might be worth something one day, but she tells me that I've been listening to my daft Grandad too much.

On the way, Nanny Pam asks me if Grandad's new girlfriend can drive. I tell her that she can, but that she always has pink lipstick on her teeth.

9am

We set up our stall. I put out all of Grandad's things and wonder if he'd be sad if he knew that Nanny Pam was selling them. A lady asks me, *How much for the Venetian Mask?* Nanny Pam tells her she can have it for 50p because it's cursed.

10am
One of Nanny Pam's weird mates comes over, he looks like Noel Edmonds, if Noel Edmonds ate twenty McDonalds every day and slept in a bin.

Hello Pamela, how much for you, sweetheart?

Alright Trev, I'm priceless love.

What you got ere then? says Trev as he looks through a pile of clothes with his Richmond Sausage fingers. *Have you worn this dressing gown in bed?*

No love, that's my ex-husbands. He thought he looked sexy in satin, but it made him sweat like a pig. It's been on a hot wash though.

Right, well, I'll just take this ashtray then please, duck. A lady friend broke the one on my bedside table last week, I won't say how.

Trev winks and laughs then starts coughing. Nanny Pam puts the ashtray in a Kwik Save bag and when he hands Nanny Pam 25p he strokes her hand a bit.

As Trev walks off there's a rank smell and I watch him shake his trouser leg to let the last of it out. I tell Nanny Pam that he makes me feel sick, Nanny Pam laughs and says that he's just a harmless perv.

12pm

We have our Sweet & Sour Pot Noodles and share a Kit Kat for lunch. Nanny Pam gives me a pound to spend while she looks after the stall. I buy a pig, because I've started collecting them; this one is a biscuit jar that has a dirty bib on saying "Greedy Pig". When I come back, I ask Nanny Pam how much she wants for the Chimpanzee cards, but she says I can have them for free!

Nanny Pam goes off and comes back with something called a Lazy Susan, and some tarot cards.

4pm

We're having a chippy tea at Nanny Pam's house to celebrate all our hard work. We use the Lazy Susan to pass each other the curry sauce. After we've finished I ask Nanny Pam if she can read my tarot cards while we eat our choc-ices.

She says I need to ask them a question, so I ask if Tom fancies me. I pull out a card with a sun on it. Nanny Pam tells me it means that love is on the horizon, but I have to read lots of books, wait a few years, and make her a coffee before it comes.

8pm

We watch Antiques Road Show with a cuppa. Nanny Pam spits her Bourbon out when the expert says some posh woman's locket is from Elizabeth Duke and is worth about a fiver. *I bet she's bloody livid, poor cow.*

I decide that I'm going to wait ten years then go on with my Chimpanzee cards, I reckon they'll be worth at least £100 by then.

EASTER

5am

It's Easter Sunday. Me and Jenny have woken up extra early because we're so excited.

We're watching Dad's *Die Hard 2* video, eating chocolate and playing a game called Smash An Egg On Your Stupid Head. We take it in turns to put a pan on our head, then drop Easter Eggs from the top of the stairs onto each other so they smash.

11am

Grandad has come over with his girlfriend, Candy. Mum and Dad are still in bed so I tell Grandad and Candy to wait on the sofa. I make them a cup of tea, but the kettle's broken so I just use water from the hot tap.

Grandad says it's the worst cuppa he has ever had in his whole life, and I'd have to learn how to make a decent one if I ever want a husband. Jenny says it's a good job we don't ever want to get married. Grandad tells her not to be cheeky.

Grandad gives us a Father Christmas shaped Easter Egg each, Candy says they're still in date.

11.20am

Mum comes downstairs and I go into the kitchen to help her

make another cup of tea for Grandad. I tell her what Grandad said to me about getting a husband. She puts a pan on to boil and says, *If you want a sexist arse of a husband like Grandad, then yeah, learn to make a good cup of tea, otherwise don't bother.*

11.30am
Grandad asks Mum if she likes Candy's new hair. Mum says, *Yeah, it's... it's very different.* Grandad asks Mum what type of fish Candy's hair is. Mum says she doesn't know what he's on about. Grandad says, *It's a Red Mullet!* and laughs on his own for a while.

12pm
The phone rings on the table next to Grandad and I answer it. It's Nanny Pam. She says she's coming round in a bit to give us our Easter eggs. I'm worried because Nanny Pam and Grandad can't stand each other, and as soon as I put the phone down Grandad starts going off on one.

If that was Pamela, tell her she owes me at least fifty quid for selling my stuff at the car boot sale. Trev saw her, said she was making a killin'! Some of that crap was priceless.

Candy says she wants to leave because she has to get home to record *Look Who's Talking* off the telly, but I think she's just scared because Nanny Pam could easily batter her.

1pm

After Grandad and Candy have left, Nanny Pam comes round with more Easter Eggs. She gives me a Crunchie one from her and Colin, and a Cadbury's Cream Egg with a fifty pence piece sellotaped to it from Auntie Maeve.

1.30pm

Nanny Pam makes an instant cappuccino and asks me about Grandad and Candy while she eats the froth with her finger. She asks if Candy wears nice clothes. I say Candy's clothes are OK, but that her hair is a type of fish, a Red Mullet, which makes Nanny Pam laugh her head off.

I tell Nanny Pam that Grandad says she owes him at least fifty quid from the car boot. She says he owes her the last twenty years of her life back, and the silver service set he nicked when he ran off with bootleg Barbie.

4pm

Me, Jenny, and Dad are sat on the sofa eating our Father Christmas Easter Eggs and watching *Father Of The Bride*. I tell Dad that I think this has been the best Easter of my life.

A PEN-GRIN

3.30pm

Dad's picking us up from school because he hasn't got a job anymore. He's stood at the back of the playground dragging his foot along the tarmac, trying to get dog shit off his shoe.

When I walk up to him he starts muttering something about the dog shit being the Tories' fault.

We get in the car. Dad gets poo all over his hand when he tries to take his shoe off. He tells Jenny she'll have to do the gears while he sticks his hand out of the sunroof. Jenny's used to doing the gears. Sometimes she sits on Dad's knee and helps drive back from Nanny Pam's house. Next year I'll be allowed to help drive too.

I love it when Dad picks me up from school. He plays his tapes really loud in the car and everyone looks at us. I pretend I'm in a music video by resting my arm on the window and looking moody, just in case Tom walks past. I'm not sure it looks as good today though, with Dad's dog shit hand sticking out of the sunroof.

4pm

As we drive up to our house we clock that Grandad's car is parked outside, Dad says, *Bollocks*. Sometimes when we see Grandad's car parked outside we drive around the block until he's gone. Last time, we hid round the back of the Happy Shopper until it was safe to go back. Mum's already let him in though, and Dad needs to wash his hand. There's no escape today.

When we walk in Grandad looks at Dad who's holding his hand in the air and trying not to touch anything.

Is that shit on your hand, you bloody idiot?

Jenny whispers to me, *Grandad's a bloody idiot.*

Dad tells her off for swearing.

Grandad and Candy have come over to talk about Auntie Mandy's wedding tomorrow. He says he's written a speech that will help him get a few things off his chest about this family. Mum has her head in her hands.

5pm
Grandad gets up to leave, Dad shakes his hand and says, *Good luck tomorrow, mate.* When he's gone, Dad tells us he used his dog poo hand to shake Grandad's. Me and Jenny laugh our heads off.

7pm
Auntie Mandy is staying over before the wedding and me and Jenny are spying on her and Mum in the kitchen. Mandy's

smoking and crying, and Mum's dipping a Penguin in her tea.

Mandy says she doesn't think she can marry a man who eats a McDonalds on a plate with knife and fork, and says, "whoops, sorry love" every time he farts.

Mum asks, *What do you call a happy penguin?*

Mandy says, *Fuck off, you're not even listening*.

I whisper to Jenny, *A pen-grin*.

9pm
Jenny says she's happy that the wedding might be off, she hates wearing dresses, and says being a bridesmaid is child labour and against her beliefs.

I tell her that I'm happy too, but I'm not. I really want to be a bridesmaid tomorrow. Nanny Pam has even promised to come round in the morning, and curl my hair with her hot rollers.

I go into Mum and Dad's room and cry while looking in the mirror like they do in music videos.

THE SPEECH

10am

Nanny Pam is curling my hair with her hot rollers in the living room. Auntie Mandy is getting ready upstairs with Mum, and Dad is trying to find his other smart shoe.

Jenny's really angry that the wedding is back on, and has said she's not going to smile all day as a peaceful protest. She's gone out the front to play in her bridesmaid dress. Nanny Pam keeps banging on the window at her, and tells her to keep off the mud.

I tell Nanny Pam about Mandy crying last night.

She says, *You can either love someone dangerously, or like someone safely, and thankfully Mandy's chosen the latter.*

I don't really understand what she means, but it still makes me feel a bit sad. I forget all about it though when Nanny Pam lets me put some blusher on.

12pm

Grandad and Candy have come round to take me and Jenny to the church with Mandy.

Grandad's tied some old ribbon to his car, but it still has all of his junk inside. I have to sit on top of a video player, and Candy has a box of garden ornaments on her lap.

Grandad has given us a go of his camcorder and I'm filming Jenny pretending to be kidnapped.

She looks at the camera and says, *Help me. They've made me wear a dress against my will. And now I have to follow the alien queen up the aisle, where she will become a slave for all eternity.*

Mandy says, *Turn that bloody thing off!*

12.30pm
We get outside the church and Jenny gets into a fight with my cousin Joe, because he laughed at our dresses. Jenny karate kicks Joe, and he punches her in the face, which makes her have a really big nosebleed.

Jenny's dress is covered in blood, and when Mandy sees her she starts crying again.

3pm
After the church, we drive to the Unicorn Club for the party bit.

Before we're allowed to start eating the buffet, we have to listen to Grandad's speech.

Firstly, I'd like to thank myself for being here today. I could barely afford the petrol after Pamela took me for all I had when we got divorced...

3.20pm

...at first, I doubted if Mandy were even mine, because Pamela always had a headache, if you know what I mean. Then, I remembered one hell of a night in Marbella, when Pamela and I had one too many Banana Breeze Cocktails at Maria's bar...

...she was gorgeous... I could have had her there and then, but Pamela pulled Maria off me, and dragged me back to the hotel.

3.30pm

...after the divorce she took everything, the car, the trouser press....

3.40pm

...even the cat bowl, and the cat died fifteen years ago...

4pm

...well, all that's left to do is wish the groom good luck. He's gonna fuckin' need it with this family.

6pm

The disco has started, and me and Nanny Pam are dancing

together. We fall over twice, but Nanny Pam just laughs her head off. I tell Nanny Pam that I love her and that Grandad's speech was a load of crap.

She says, *Grandad's why you should be very careful about falling in love.*

DAD AND THE RAT

4pm

Even before I get to our block, on my way back from school, I can hear Jenny on her pogo stick out the front. Mum let her skive school today, because she wasn't sure if it's non-school uniform day. Last time she forgot and had to sit with the teachers at lunchtime to stop everyone taking the piss.

Ever since Jenny got the pogo stick for her birthday, she's been showing off on it. Mum even let her eat her dinner on it last week. I had to pass her a battered sausage and each chip one at a time.

When she sees me she says, *I'm setting a new world record! If I stay on here another half hour, I'll have smashed my last one.* I keep telling her it's not an official record unless Cheryl Baker's there to time it, but she doesn't listen.

I go up to the house and Mum answers the door. She puts her finger to her lips and tells me to *ssshhhhh!*

Dad's in the living room with his big green parka on, holding a gun.

Last week, we saw a rat eating Tosca's cat food. Dad hasn't got a job at the moment, so he's spent the whole week trying to shoot the rat with an air rifle that he borrowed off Uncle Tony.

4.15pm

I go into the kitchen to make a cup of tea for me and Dad and get us a Mint Viscount each. Nanny Pam's round and she's chatting to Mum who's making fish in a bag for dinner.

I ask Nanny Pam if she wants a biscuit but she says, *No thanks love, I'm saving all my Weight Watchers points for the all you can eat at Wing Wa's on Friday night. Me and Colin have been starving ourselves all week. For tea last night all we had was a cuppa soup and a choc ice!*

4.20pm

Dad's by the backdoor, pointing the air rifle into the garden. I sit down next to him and we both stare at Tosca's cat bowl in silence for a bit.

Dad asks me if I had a good day at school. I tell him it was OK, apart from everyone being immature as usual. Today, they were all going on about the word "blowjob". Sammy asked me if I'd ever had a blowjob, and Kevin asked me if I was a blowjob. Then someone made a song up about a blowjob, and everyone went around singing it in the playground until the dinner ladies lost it at them.

I tell Dad that I don't actually know what the word even means, but, if it's anything like the wanker word, I don't want to. Dad says I won't ever need to know what it means and then asks me if anything good happened today.

I tell Dad that the best bit of today was when a dog went on to the school field in the afternoon. Everyone went crazy! Sammy screamed and said, *It's a dog, it's a dog,* like a stupid idiot that's never seen a dog before. Then they all got bored, and I watched him on my own for the rest of the afternoon through the classroom window.

I don't tell Dad that I also managed to get the reflection from my Jurassic Park watch to shine on Mr. Moore's head in assembly this morning, which was funny for a bit, until I started to feel sorry for him.

4.30pm
I ask Dad if he thinks we should lay some more bait out for the rat. We both agree that a rat might like Bacon Frazzles, so I go back into the kitchen to get some.

Nanny Pam's talking to Mum about Dad. She asks if he can get work in Germany again. Mum says he can, but he doesn't want to be away from the kids and he's been too busy with the rat stuff anyway. Nanny Pam asks Mum how she's going to get the boiler fixed with no money coming in.

For the last few months, the boiler has been broken. It's been OK though, and it's summer, so we don't have to wear our coats in bed like last time. To have a bath we all run up the stairs with loads of kettles and pans of hot water to fill it up. But most of the time, Mum heats up a big pan of water and puts it in front of the TV in the living room. Then, Jenny and our little brother, Josh, and me, all take it in turns to stand in it with a flannel. The rule is you do your face first and bum last. I don't know what Nanny Pam's on about. It's OK not having a boiler. When does she ever get to have a wash in front of the TV?

4.40pm
BANG!!!!

We all run up to the backdoor to look for the dead rat, but it isn't there. Dad says he shot it, and it ran into Carol's garden, next-door, to die.

I feel really sad. A bit because of the rat, but mostly about Dad going back to Germany now that it's dead.

4.50pm
There's a knock at the front door, and I answer it. It's Nanny Pam's boyfriend, Colin. He's been to Macro and gives me a massive tub of fizzy cola bottles, which makes me feel a bit better.

5pm
We all sit at the table and eat dinner. Jenny tells everyone

about her world records, Nanny Pam tries to work out how many points are in a potato waffle, and Josh puts bits of fish flakes in his orange squash then drinks it.

Colin stares into the garden and asks, *Is that a rat eating Tosca's cat food?'*

AMERICA

9.30am

I'm having a day off school, because my class are on a school trip to Coventry FC's ground and Mum said that I'd get a better education staying at home today.

Nanny Pam has come round to look after me and we are sat on the sofa watching Supermarket Sweep. Nanny Pam shouts at the lady on the TV, *Quiches are in the fridges, you daft cow!*

9.35am

We hear a man coughing up a greenie outside the front door. It's Grandad.

Grandad has been away in America for a few weeks after he split up with Candy. Mum said Candy was sick of living in Grandad's static caravan full of his useless old crap.

I open the door. Grandad's wearing cowboy boots, shorts and a shirt with topless women holding guitars on it.

Nanny Pam laughs her head off when she sees. *I've seen it all now.*

Pammy, I'm a new man. I think you're going to start regretting kicking this cowboy out!

Nanny Pam says, *I'm going into the kitchen to make a coffee,
when I come back in I want to watch This Morning in peace,
without you here.*

9.50am
Grandad sits down, lights a cigar and starts watching
Supermarket Sweep, he shouts at the lady, *Go for the
electricals, you daft cow!*

The cigar smells so bad I have to put my nose into my Count
Dukula t-shirt to be able to breathe.

10.00am
When Supermarket Sweep finishes, Grandad tells me he's not
used to such crap telly, or small couches, or tiny houses like this.
He says the bog in his hotel was bigger than our living room.
Then he gives me a present. It's a pen that says "I GOT LUCKY
IN LAS VEGAS X".

I ask him lots of questions like: Did he go to a Prom? Is the
McDonalds the same? Did he have a corn dog? Did he have a
telly on the plane?

Grandad says all I need to know is that America is bigger,
brighter and better than this shit hole.

10.05am

Nanny Pam comes back in with a cup of coffee and a mint choc Options for me.

This Morning has started, and Nanny Pam turns to Grandad.

Times up Skint Eastwood! Judy's waxing Richard's leg in a minute, and I don't want you ruining it by talking silly bollocks about America.

We were like Richard and Judy once.

If you mean I was the long suffering wife of an arrogant arsehole then I suppose we were, now bugger off.

GRANDAD'S SHOP

8am

It's Saturday and I'm sniffing Joop in Mum and Dad's room. Dad has got a job, but it means he has to live in Germany and we only get to see him once a month.

Last week I sprayed Joop on my school jumper so I could smell Dad all day. Sammy said I smelled like her Uncle Barry though, and everyone called me Uncle Barry for the rest of the week, so now I just stick to sniffing the bottle.

8.30am

Mum's working in Grandad's shop today. He gave Auntie Mandy the sack last week for giving Uncle Steve a discount, and begged mum to work last night. We have to go too because Nanny Pam's in Tenerife and can't look after us.

9.30am

We get to Grandad's shop and see him having a fag outside. He blocks the door to the shop with his leg, so we can't go in. Then he tells us his list of shop rules:

1. Don't call me Grandad, there are lots of lovely young ladies round 'ere that think I'm still in me forties.
2. Don't touch anything!
3. Don't go near the aisle closest to the back door!

4. You can have one bag of pic-n-mix each, but don't take the piss, none of the posh stuff with wrappers on. And don't open the tub of foam bananas, I trapped a fly in there yesterday and I don't think the bastard's dead yet.

10am

The inside of Grandad's shop smells like wee and Dettol. There's junk everywhere, and Grandad has made some of the shelves himself out of stacked up old fag boxes and planks of wood.

Grandad sells all sorts, fishing rods, tin openers, bin bags and loads of fake stuff... We try on some Roy Ban sunglasses and Jenny sprays on some Melvin Klein perfume. I smell the bottle that looks like Joop but it's called Dupe and it doesn't smell anything like Dad.

I ask Jenny what she thinks is in the aisle we're not allowed in. Jenny says it's probably guns, tear gas and grenades, but I think she's just saying that because she's been learning about World War One at school.

11am

An old lady asks Mum at the till if she can have a discount on a plate because it has a crack in.

Grandad overhears, snatches the plate off Mum then smashes it on the floor. *You can have it for free, love!*

Mum tries to apologise, but the old lady mutters something about Grandad burning in hell and walks out of the shop.

Grandad shouts after her, *Don't bother coming back unless you can afford the price tag, you tight-arsed old cow.*

12pm
Grandad has gone out to the cash and carry and Mum is sorting out the rental videos near the front of the shop.

Me and Jenny leave Josh in the gardening aisle with a little stone hedgehog and a bag of pic-n-mix. Then we sneak to the aisle nearest the back door.

There is lots of dressing up stuff for grown-ups. One of the outfits is really shiny and looks like a cross between a police woman and a swimming costume, and the lady on the packaging has lots of make-up on. Jenny passes me a candle that is shaped like a willy and I pretend to do a wee with it.

There's loads of other weird stuff too, on one shelf there's a massive weird shaped glass thing called "King Bong" next to condoms. Jenny told me what condoms do last year, but neither of us can work out what the Pina-Colada flavoured ones on the shelf are for.

1pm

Grandad comes back with lunch. He's holding a bag of chips in one hand and is picking his nose with the other.

He serves the chips up with his hands and puts them on paper plates for us all. Jenny and me inspect each chip for bogeys before we eat them. Mum doesn't eat anything.

4pm

Grandad gives mum some money for working, but says that he's taking off the money for the chips, so she only gets a tenner. I feel really angry at Grandad. I wouldn't have eaten any of those bogey chips if I knew mum had to pay for them. When Grandad's not looking, Me and Jenny stuff a load of posh pic-n-mix into our pockets to get back at him.

6pm

We get home and Mum lets us ring Dad. When it's Jenny's turn to speak, she tells him all about the funny outfits in Grandad's shop. I know she's told Dad on purpose so he won't let us go there again.

I tell Dad that I miss him and read him the postcard Nanny Pam sent us from Tenerife. He laughs when I tell him the bit about Colin eating a dodgy roast dinner at the beach bar, and losing a stone in one night.

6.30pm

Mum has locked her bedroom door and we can hear her crying. Jenny says it's because Grandad's been an arsehole and she misses Dad. We push posh pic 'n' mix under her door until she lets us in, then we snuggle and watch Blind Date.

THE DISCO

5pm

Mum is helping me get ready for the Christmas disco. I'm wearing a black velvet skirt with an orange velvet crop top and Mum has crimped my hair and sprayed it with glitter.

I use one of Mum's Avon perfume samples called "Timeless". I'm not sure if I smell nice or not, because Jenny says that I smell like Toilet Duck. I think Jenny's just jealous though. She has to stay in and look at the new Next catalogue with Mum and Nanny Pam all night, because she's too old to come to the disco.

5.30pm

Dad's back from Germany but I still have to get a lift with Grandad, because Dad's car broke down outside Londis last week and we can't afford to fix it.

Grandad is late! His car is full of all his usual junk from car boot sales, but this time there's a load of Christmas stuff too. I have to sit with a Father Christmas doll on my lap that dances and plays "Another Rock 'N' Roll Christmas" when you press its belly.

Grandad makes me hold the seatbelt in the socket the whole way, because he says it's buggered, and he keeps singing the same line from a really annoying Christmas song:

Driving home for Christmas... in me car... driving home for Christmas.

When we pull up to the school, I can see Tom standing outside the gate. I hide behind the Father Christmas doll, which starts singing and dancing again. Tom looks really good. He's had his haircut; it's all shaved apart from a fringe, which he's gelled into points.

Grandad asks me what I'm hiding for, then he sees Tom and says, *There's something you should know about fellas, sweetheart, we're only after one thing. You don't want to end up getting knocked up like your mother did. We like you now love, but you and your sister were massive, massive mistakes. OK, have fun. I might be able to pick you up later.*

6.00pm

I walk into school. It feels funny seeing it in the dark. In the corridor outside the school hall some of the teachers are selling orange squash and sweets. The teachers are dressed in their normal teacher clothes except they have jeans on. The only grown-up who's made an effort is Mr. Haywood, the caretaker. He's wearing a sequinned waistcoat, a piano tie, and a light up Father Christmas hat.

While I wait for Amy to come and meet me, I have an orange squash to calm my nerves. Amy hates school as much as I do and I had to beg her to come to the disco. I told her how much I wanted Tom to see me in my velvet outfit and that we could practice our dancing.

When Amy gets here I have another squash with her and we go into the hall together. The DJ is rubbish. He keeps saying stupid things on his microphone, like, I can't hear you guys having F F F Fun. I'm not even sure he's a real DJ, he looks like Natalie's dad with sunglasses on. The lights look really cool though, and me and Amy try and stamp on the same light as it moves around the room.

The DJ says, *Here's your first slowy of the night for all you L L L Lovebirds* and starts playing the song from *Robin Hood*. Me and Amy start singing along really loudly in a cheesy way, but everyone else starts to walk around slowly and boys and girls start dancing with each other. I look around for Tom and he's dancing with Sammy. My eyes start to sting a bit, so I ask Amy if she wants another drink.

The song lasts ages, I manage to have three more squashes before it's even finished. When I get home, I'm writing "Robin Hood Song" on the list of things I hate in the back of my diary, it can go under "Cheese Strings" and "liars".

6.30pm
Finally, "YMCA" starts playing and we quickly finish our

drinks and go back into the hall to dance.

After "Superman" and "Wig Wam Bam", the DJ plays "Saturday Night" by Whigfield, everyone gets into lines and starts doing the dance. I start to feel a bit weird, but I keep dancing. Halfway through, my tummy feels horrible. I do the bit where you jump and clap, then I start chundering all over the place. A lot of people don't see and carry on dancing, then they start slipping in the orange sick until it gets everywhere, and the hall's evacuated.

7pm
I'm sat on a bench in the hall with Amy, my teacher Mrs. Woods, and a bucket. Everyone else is in the corridor apart from the DJ who has taken his sunnies off (deffo Natalies Dad), and Mr. Haywood, who is cleaning up the sick with a mop. Mr. Haywood's taken his sequinned waistcoat off and is whistling along to "Last Christmas". I feel really sad watching him and start to cry a bit.

7.30pm
Most people have gone home, but I'm still stood outside the school gate waiting for Grandad to pick me up. Tom is waiting by the gate for his lift too. I'm not in the mood to try and show off to him, so I just concentrate on smoothing out the damp velvet on my skirt where the sick was.

Tom asks me why I was sick. I tell him I had too much to drink, which makes it sound like I was drunk, which I think sounds better.

Tom says that it looked mint when everyone was skidding in the sick. I tell him I saw Mrs. Woods fall over in it (even though I didn't). Tom laughs and says it was the best bit of the disco.

7.45pm
Grandad pulls up and shouts out of his car window, *She's not interested in lads who can only afford half a haircut and can't even give her a lift home*. I get in the car. Tom waves at me and I wave back. I think that Tom can't fancy Sammy that much if he likes me being sick more than dancing with her.

Grandad starts singing again, but I don't even care. I think that this might be the best night of my life.

JACKIE'S MARVELOUS MEDICINE

3.00pm

Me and my little brother Josh are playing out with the kids who live on the next block, Kaleigh-Anne and Levi. Kaleigh-Anne is my age and her brother Levi is the same age as Josh. The whole of Eastern Green calls their family "the Jackie Potatoes", because their mum's name is Jackie and their dad looks like a potato.

Everybody says the Jackie Potatoes are nutters, and that when Potato disappeared for six months last year he was in prison for nicking rare bird eggs, but there's no way he'd get up a tree!

Jackie is really shouty, even when she's being nice she shouts things like, DO YOUSE WANT ANY SQUASH?. I don't mind her though. She sometimes buys us McDonalds when we go round and lets us go on her running machine in the garage. She's really thin, has black hair that she spikes up at the back, and always wears heels, even her slippers have heels on! I think that she could be anywhere between thirty and sixty years old; she wears so much make-up you can't see her real face.

Potato eats Doritos and watches Sky Sports all day with the curtains shut, I've never heard him speak or even seen him move (there's no way he'd get up a tree!).

Me and Kaleigh-Anne are helping the boys build a den out

of the grass that's just been cut on their block. The boys are collecting all the grass and we're making walls.

3.15pm
Josh starts crying. When I look round there's a load of older kids from Tile Hill with water guns, they've soaked Josh and now they've started on Levi who has run onto his front lawn and is banging the door for Jackie to let him in.

Jackie opens the door and goes totally nuts at the Tile Hill lot. They laugh at her and call her a mouthy cow, which makes her turn red and lob one of her heels them. Once we've all ran inside Jackie slams the door. From the blurry porch window we can see the Tile Hill kids sitting on the grass out the front. They wreck the boy's den and start squirting the neighbours' windows.

3.30pm
Jackie smokes loads of fags to calm down and Potato switches from the football to the cricket.

Jackie Potato's house is like ours on the outside, but inside it's really different. Everywhere has flowery wallpaper that's gone yellow, and there's a light up picture of Jesus next to Jackie's ashtray on the coffee table. Above the electric fire there's a massive family photo that they got done in West Orchards Shopping Centre. In it, Jackie and Kayleigh-Anne are wearing matching pink dresses, Levi's in a little suit, and Potato is in the massive John Smiths t-shirt he always wears.

Jackie says she recognised one of the lads, and that his mum works on the make-up counter in Debenhams. I think she's going to phone his Mum up at Debenhams but she comes up with another plan.

3.35pm
We all go into the garage with Jackie and she digs out two Supersoakers and some water bombs, which we take into the kitchen. Jackie gets a massive jug out of a cupboard and tells us all to fill it with any liquid we can think of. Jackie pours in a load of milk and I put some Robinson's Tropical Fruits in, then Levi adds some vinegar. Kayleigh-Anne gets some Toilet Duck out from the cupboard under the sink, but Jackie says, *I ain't going back to court for those little shits!* and makes her put it back.

3.50pm
Me and Kayleigh-Anne help to fill up the Supersoakers and water-bombs with Jackie's Marvelous Medicine. I start to think that maybe Jackie is a proper nutter and that I might need to take Josh home.

Before I can make up an excuse Jackie starts shoving me into one of the yellow macs you get free on the log flume at Drayton Manor. I look round and Kayleigh-Anne has one on too.

Jackie hands us a water gun each and pushes us out the door.

The Tile Hill kids laugh their heads off when they see us and start shooting water at me and Kayleigh-Anne. We start pumping up the water guns slowly at first, but when they start calling us soggy slags we go for it! Kayleigh-Anne's ready before me and starts shooting at them.

They keep laughing at us, and the girls in the gang do really stupid screams and tell the boys that they're wet. Then when they realise their tops are stained and they smell like tropical milk and vinegar, they stop laughing and start screaming.

Jackie comes up behind us laughing like crazy. Levi and Josh are handing her water bombs and she's lobbing them at the kids who have started to run away.

Josh tries to chase one of the boys with a water bomb and trips. The boy turns back and starts kicking Josh. We all jump on him, but he won't stop kicking. I start screaming and crying, but before I can run to our block to get help, Potato comes out and grabs the boy by his feet. Jackie grabs his arms and they drag him down the grass toward the brook. Potato has dark green circles around his armpits on his t-shirt and sounds like he's just run a marathon after smoking a thousand fags. (THERE'S NO WAY HE'D GET UP A TREE!!!)

I start worrying about the boy. I've fallen in the brook loads. It's not very deep so you can't drown in it, but when I have fallen in, Mum's made me have a bath with a whole bottle of Dettol in because she says there's rat wee in the brook. What if the boy doesn't know about Dettol?

When they get to the brook the boy is crying and shaking, they let go of him right by the edge and he gets up and legs it.

I grab Josh and start legging it too!

4.00pm

When we get home Josh is still a bit teary so Mum makes his favourite snack: a fairy sandwich (white bread, butter, hundreds of thousands). I tell Mum all about Jackie and she says Kayleigh-Anne and Levi can come and play round ours next time.

TWO LIONS ON THE SHIRT

6.00pm

We're going to watch the football at Grandad's new house tonight. I haven't seen Grandad in ages. Mum said he went away and got some money and now he's back and has bought a big new house in Solihull. Candy has started going out with him again, and they've had a baby! So, today, I'm going to meet my baby uncle, Gary.

6.30pm

We pull up to Grandad's house. There's a drive and the front door has pillars outside! Dad asks Mum, *What's he done to pull this off?*

Grandad has a tan, and even more gold jewellery on than usual. He gives us a tour of the house. There are five bedrooms and a Jacuzzi outside! Jenny asks Grandad if we can go in, but he says he's not wasting a tenner heating it up for us to piss in it.

In Grandad's bedroom there's a giant picture of Candy in a bikini kissing a dolphin. Grandad points at a smaller photo of him on the bedside table, in it he's got even more of a tan and dreadlocks. He says, *That's me, dressed as Bob Marley at a Jamaican night in the Costa Del Sol... bloody brilliant it was! Candy went as Jamaican Cher!'*

7.00pm

The football is on in the living room. Uncle Gary is sleeping in his car seat in the corner, and Grandad's mate, Ladders, is sitting on the sofa with one hand holding a pint of Carling and the other down his joggers.

England are playing Germany in the semi-final. Grandad and Ladders keep singing the Dad's Army theme tune. I think they're both drunk, because there are beer cans everywhere, and when Ladders gets up to shout at the TV he sways and forgets what he's shouting at.

Me and Jenny practice our goal celebrations. Jenny is going over the top as usual, she does a cartwheel and ends in the splits. I do a star jump and clap.

8.15pm

At half time Candy comes into the living room holding a cake she's made and says, *Happy football day, everybody! Look, it's shaped like a football especially.*

Grandad says, *What... round? Aren't all cakes round anyway?*

Well, yeah, but... oh shut up, you tosser!

Grandad snaps a big bit off with his hand and eats it, then he says, *Candy, what did you use to make this cake?*

You know I used the packet mix I bought from Londis, you were there! What are you getting at?

Oh nothing, sweetheart, it just tastes like you made it out of dog shit, that's all.

Ladders sniffs the cake, pulls a stupid face at Grandad, as if he's dying, then asks Candy, *Any of them mint Clubs left?*

Candy slams the cake down in front of Grandad's feet on the coffee table, and storms off into the kitchen.

8.30pm
Grandad says he's got me and Jenny an England shirt each. He goes into the cupboard under the stairs and pulls out a bin bag, then chucks a shirt at Jenny.

Nobody's eating the cake, so I help myself, to make Candy feel better, and because I quite like the taste of really salty stuff anyway.

Grandad says to me, *I've only got XL left for you Hol, but you'll soon grow into it, the way you're putting that cake away. I'm sorry to say it, love, but it looks like you've got the family fat genes off your Nan.*

I say, *Nanny Pam's not fat!*

No, love, but she could be if she ate more.

I have no idea what Grandad's on about. I think about whether I'm fat and whether Tom thinks I'm fat. I don't feel fat, but I stop eating the cake just in case.

The shirts don't look like the ones everyone has at school. We put them on and start singing "Three lions on a shirt..." then Jenny points out our shirts only have two lions and they look more like beavers.

9pm

Ladders wakes up Uncle Gary by shouting and swearing at the TV. Candy lets me hold him for a bit. He's fat and tiny at the same time and his face is all squashed up and red like Grandad's. He grabs my finger in his little fist, and I sing the Football's Coming Home song to him, which I think he likes, because he kicks his fat little legs.

10pm

England lose, and Grandad kicks off. He says, *I was there when the bombs were coming down, those cheeky little fuckers still owe us one!*

Mum says, *You were born in 1946, Dad! Now stop swearing and being a racist prick in front of the kids!*

Ladders is definitely drunk. He's been on the floor since the penalties started, when he fell over showing Grandad how to take one. Grandad gets a big bottle of red booze from the shelf above the TV. He opens Ladders' mouth and starts pouring it in, then he asks Dad, *Who does Ladders remind you of?*

Dad says, *Right, it's time to go, get your shoes on kids.*

Grandad says, *He's Gazza, you know, doing the dentist chair.*

Ladders is coughing and laughing at the same time, and the booze is going all over his face and the carpet.

Candy comes in, looks at Grandad sat on top of Ladders, and shouts, *Get the fuck out, you two!* Then she looks at me and says all nice, *Holly, do you want to take the rest of that cake home, sweetheart, you looked like you were really enjoying it?*

10.30pm
In the car on the way home, Dad says that we're never going round Grandad's house again, but he always says that. Me and Jenny sing, "Two lions on the shirt", and do impressions of Ladders pretending to be Gazza.

LEANNE

10am

It's Saturday. Mum and Dad have gone to Carpet Right, and my cousin Leanne has come round to look after us and do Mum's ironing.

Jenny and Josh are playing Hungry Hippos. I'm not playing because Josh is cheating by grabbing all the balls and shoving them in his hippo's mouth.

I lie upside down on the sofa with my head touching the floor, and talk to Leanne while she does the ironing. I ask her lots of questions like: Is she still going out with Swanny Kid? Does she like lasagne? Does Swanny Kid like lasagne? Has she ever been on a dual carriageway?

She just answers yes or no, until I ask her what Swanny Kid's real name is. She says it's really Wes, but he's been called Swanny Kid ever since Tall Paul said his mum looks like a Swan. She always wears a white jacket, has a long neck, and uses a lot of black eye make-up.

10.30am

Leanne puts her headphones on. I ring Nanny Pam and ask her what she's up to. She's going to look at bathrooms in Homebase with Colin, she says I can come but I say I don't want to. The last time I went to Homebase with Nanny Pam, we were there for three hours! And they wouldn't even let me go to Pet City next door afterwards because Colin doesn't like the snakes.

My cousin Joe says he taught the parrot in Pet City the F-word, but Nanny Pam told me that's a load of rubbish, it can only say Hello and the S-word.

10.45am

I ring Auntie Mandy to ask her what number the Horoscopes are on Teletext. Her home number just keeps ringing, so I call the work one in the address book. She tells me that I should write the numbers down, and that I can't keep ringing her at work just to see what Mystic Meg has to say.

11.00am

I read my horoscope. It says, "A situation at work is heating up, and I'll have to confront it before I can move on." I think it means that Tom fancies me.

I play Bamboozle for a bit but I don't know any of the answers and Leanne pretends she can't hear me when I ask her what the capital of Sweden is.

12.00pm

I go into the kitchen to make myself some lunch, there's not much food in the house, so I just make a salt and butter batch.

I make one for Leanne too, but she only has a few bites.

3pm

Mum and Dad come back, I tell them that this has been the most boring day of my life. Dad says he's had the most boring day of his life too, at Carpet Right.

I go upstairs and look out the window for a bit with Jenny. Our next-door neighbour Carol is in her garden, we like to spy on her sometimes to see what she's up to. Jenny says she saw her digging a big hole in her garden a few weeks ago.

4pm

Dad tells us to come downstairs. He's set up a game of Gladiators in the living room. Dad's Wolf, Josh is Shadow, Mum's John Anderson and Jenny and me are the contenders. We play until Josh falls asleep on the Travelator, which is a duvet on the stairs.

ROXY'S HOUSE

3.30pm

Every other Thursday, Nanny Pam can't pick us up from school because she has a shift on the fag counter in Tesco. This means my friend Roxy's nan, Maggie, has to pick us up. Me and Jenny have started calling Maggie "Skeletor" behind her back because she's dead thin and dead moody.

Maggie waits outside of school in her car and beeps the horn until we get in. The car smells like cigarettes, fir tree air freshener and digestive biscuits, and she's playing her Robson and Jerome tape.

Dad hates Robson and Jerome. He says they're one of the reasons he wants us to move abroad. Me and Jenny say we hate them too, but I actually love it when they come on; their song makes me think of Tom and I feel sad in a happy way.

Maggie tells Jenny and me that we didn't look both ways when we crossed the road to get to her car, and she'll have to tell Mum, because it's a safety hazard. I'm sat in the front and Maggie makes me hold her cigarette, while she starts the car. I waft the smoke away with my book about the Vikings.

4pm

We get back to Roxy's house and go upstairs to her bedroom.

Roxy says she lives with her Nan because her mum stays out too late and doesn't have a settee.

We play with Roxy's toys for a bit. All of Roxy's Barbies have shaved heads and tattoos that she has drawn on with felt tips. Roxy says she wants to play Blind Date with naked Barbies who are alcoholics. I ask if we can see her hamsters, Bill and Ted, instead, and she takes them out for me.

When we're called for tea Roxy shuts the hamsters in a tiny drawer by her bed, because she says she wants them to have babies and they need to spend time together.

5pm

I'm worried when I see dinner, because it's a burger with chips and beans. Mum says we can't eat burgers because of mad cow disease. I remind Jenny after she has had a bite, and we both say we're not eating it. Maggie says we're ungrateful, and that in the war she had to eat her pet rabbit Floppsy, with two mouldy potatoes and her own tears, and it was the best meal she ever had.

Maggie sits with us and makes us eat some chips, while she has a cigarette and drinks a Slimfast.

5.45pm

I say I'm going to the toilet, but really I go to Roxy's room and put the hamsters back in their cage.

6pm

Mum comes and picks us up. On the way home, I tell her about Maggie trying to kill us. Mum says we were right to not eat the burger, but we should have just chopped it up and hidden it under the beans.

She asks us if we crossed the road properly. I say we did, but Maggie couldn't see because her car was so full of smoke it was like Stars In Their Eyes.

Jenny says in Maggie's voice, *Tonight, Matthew, I'm going to be Skeletor.*

SMOKING WITH GRANDAD

11am

Some older kids have started hanging out on the green in front of our house. They're all dressed in black, and Jenny says that they're called Goths. One of them is called Tasha, and the other day she started talking to me. I like her; we hate the same things, like school, Baby Spice, and orange Tic-Tacs.

Tasha said she would call on me today and we could hang out together, so I'm getting ready. I find my long black velvet skirt that I usually wear with my orange velvet top to school discos and family parties, but today I'm going to wear it with Jenny's black shirt that I've just started fitting into. I look in Mum and Dad's chest of drawers for anything else that's black and find Dad's black tie he wears for job interviews and funerals.

11.30am

I go downstairs and ask Dad if I can borrow his tie and if he can put it on for me. Dad asks, *Are you sure you want to wear this Hol? It's thirty degrees outside.* I tell Dad that I'm sure. I don't think Dad really gets goths.

Mum and Dad said I could hang out with Tasha as long as I stay on the green outside our house where they can see me.

12.00pm

When Tasha knocks at the door, I run downstairs to answer it. She's wearing a long black coat and has loads of black make-up on.

We sit on the green for a bit and talk about things we hate. Tasha says that she needs to go to Happy Shopper, because it's the only place that will serve her fags. I look back at my house. When I left, Mum was writing an essay for college, and Dad was sat in the paddling pool, so I decide that they won't notice me leave the green.

Tasha asks me if I've ever smoked, I lie and tell her I did on holiday last year. She passes me the fag she's smoking and I put it in my mouth. Tasha tells me to inhale, but I hold my breath and take it out again because I don't want cancer.

Tasha talks about all the things she thinks are tragic for a bit, which is pretty much anything. Happy Shopper is tragic, a man picking up a dog shit outside Threshers is tragic, a window cleaner across the road is tragic, and people who like Terry's Chocolate Oranges are tragic.

1.00pm

I feel sick when I see Grandad's car pull up. He gets out of his car, kicks the door shut and starts walking towards the shop. I think he's going to walk straight past, but he stops just before the entrance and sees me.

Bloody hell Hol! I didn't recognise you there love. Why are you dressed like a vampire at a court appearance?

I shrug my shoulders and remember the fag in my hand, which I pass back to Tasha.

I'm just picking up a few tins, but I'll give you both a lift home if you hang on.

When Grandad comes out the shop, we get in his car. It's full of more crap than ever. This time there's a load of videos that say "Titanic" on them in Grandad's handwriting. Grandad says, *Have you seen that film yet Hol? You can give your friend a copy, if you like. It's not even out in Blockbusters yet! You'll have to excuse the bit around two hours in though, where a shadow gets up to go to the bog, that bits not meant to be in the film.*

Tasha says she doesn't want a copy because cheesy Hollywood films like that are tragic.

Grandad says, *You're bloody right it's tragic, love! Over fifteen hundred people died on that boat... unsinkable my arse! Candy still cries when she watches it, and she's seen it twelve times!*

Grandad won't shut up. I feel really hot. I pull Dad's tie to undo it, but it just makes it tighter and when I try to wind the window down the handle comes off in my hand.

And that poor bird Rose losing her boyfriend Jack like that, she went on to be a pilot and do all sorts, you know, and she's still alive today!

I say, *I think they made that bit up for the film, Grandad.*

Fuckin' ell Hol, the Titanic's not just a film you know! This shit happened, I tell you what I'm bloody glad I don't pay any tax, it'd be wasted on your shite arse education.

I want Grandad to stop talking, so I don't argue with him.

Anyway Hol, I noticed you were smoking outside the shop, and I'm not one to stop you. Forty a day for forty years and look at me, apart from the asthma, psoriasis and angina, I'm doing pretty well for fifty-one. So, love, help yourself to the fags in the back. I got a load of them from Turkey. They're practically giving them away out there. Candy said she wants a new extension and I said I'd build her one out of fag boxes, I've got that many of em!

Grandad looks at me in his car mirror, *You hear that, Hol? I said I'd build an extension for Candy out of fag boxes... anyway, go on light up.*

Tasha shoves loads of fags into her bag and then lights one for us both. I just hold it and feel hotter than ever, and like I might be sick and choke to death at the same time.

1.20pm
Tasha asks if she can get dropped off at hers on the way back. She lives in one of the big new houses near the Co-op and her front garden has a gnome playing golf on it. She jumps out the car and shouts at us, *Cheers for the fags, yeah!*

Grandad turns to me and says, *How are you feeling love? You're looking a bit peaky. You won't wanna knock around smokin' with Tuesday Addams anymore will yer? And what were you doing outside Happy Shopper? There's some right scrotes hangin' round there.*

I start crying and tell Grandad I just want to go home.

1.30pm
We get back to my house.

Mum asks me where I have been, and says that she was really worried. Grandad says, *She's been with me. I gave her and Rocky Horror a lift to the shops.*

She stinks of bloody smoke, Dad. I told you I don't want you chainin' it around the kids anymore. I'm sick of having to wash their clothes every time they see you.

Grandad says that he's sorry, and winks at me.

AUNTIE MANDY

4pm

Auntie Mandy has come to stay with us for a few days. She's fallen out with Uncle Simon again.

Auntie Mandy has been sleeping at ours a lot over the last few months. I secretly love it when she rings up crying her eyes out asking if she can stay again. She's really fun and I've been learning loads about her that I didn't know before like:

1. Auntie Mandy loves reading. By her bed she has loads of books like *Love on Death Row*, *Sexy Psychopaths* and *Married to a Monster*.

2. Apart from Nanny Pam, Auntie Mandy is the only person I know who watches Channel 5. Sometimes I sneak into her room when everyone's gone to bed and we watch strange documentaries. Last night, we watched one about dead pets that come back and haunt their owners.

3. Auntie Mandy never puts the big light on. She sleeps in Josh's room when she comes to stay and lights loads of candles. She says it's better "Fung Shay", but I think she does it so she can't see the Power Rangers on Josh's wallpaper.

Mum's in the kitchen washing up and I'm sat on the side eating a packet of Jaffa Cakes. I bite the disgusting jelly bits off first, hold my nose, and swallow them whole so I can enjoy the rest of them.

I ask mum, *Why's Auntie Mandy fallen out with Uncle Simon this time?*

Oh I don't know Hol, and don't go asking her, she needs some space so just leave her alone tonight, yeah?

4.10pm
I'm sat at the end of Auntie Mandy's bed finishing off the Jaffa Cakes. I think about what to say for a bit, but I don't want there to be a big fat elephant in the room so I just ask her.

Why did you fall out with Uncle Simon this time?

We didn't really fall out, Hol. Si doesn't know how to fall out. Whenever I try and have a row with him he just shuts himself in the spare room with his model cruise ships and whistles the Big Break theme tune until I stop shouting. He's just really REALLY BORING and I'm really REALLY BORED!

5pm
Auntie Mandy's teaching me how to make your face look really tanned with loads of make-up when the doorbell goes. It's Uncle Simon.

We can hear Uncle Simon in the porch talking to mum. *It's got warm again. I didn't know whether to wear my jacket today because it was a bit nippy this morning, so I wore it anyway and just took it off when it got a bit warmer.*

Auntie Mandy gets into bed and puts her head under Josh's Power Rangers duvet.

I ask her if she's OK and she muffles, *Tell him to fuck off. No, wait tell him I'm really ill with a tummy bug, yeah tell him that, he hates tummy bugs!*

5.30pm

Uncle Simon's in the garden having a cuppa with Dad. Dad thinks Uncle Simon is really boring too and usually when Uncle Simon comes round Dad says he's got to fix something in the garage. There are no tools to fix anything with in the garage, just a thousand bikes, a manky old tent and everything that has ever broken in our house. Last time I went to look for Dad when Uncle Simon was round, he was sat on a broken exercise bike reading his *Viz*.

I walk up to Uncle Simon and tell him that Auntie Mandy has a tummy bug and can't be more than a metre away from the bog, which means she can't see him.

Uncle Simon says, *Oh dear, yeah I'll steer clear of that one. I hate tummy bugs, last time I got one I had to move back in with my mother because she's got a more powerful cistern.*

You have to wait for ours to refill, which is a nightmare if you need a double flush.

Dad asks me if I've been painting a fence because my face is covered in Ron Seal, I tell him, *It's "Desert Island Mystique Bronzer" by Avon, actually!*

I think Dad must feel sorry for Uncle Simon today because he hasn't gone to the garage yet and he even asks Uncle Simon about football, which he hates!

Did you see the football?

Which game?

I don't know.

Then they just sit in silence for a bit.

6.15pm
After a while, Uncle Simon starts telling Dad about how he's decided that he still doesn't like tomatoes because he had a BLT at the Beefeater on Tuesday night and it had a tomato in and he didn't like it.

Dad says that he's got to fix something in the garage.

6.20pm

Mum comes out to the garden with another cup of tea for Uncle Simon and one of the dodgy boxes of chocolates Grandad gave us for Christmas. There are no menu cards and when me and Jenny ate a box only two were nice, the rest of them tasted like dog chocolate. There are still twenty-six boxes under Mum's bed, so anytime someone comes round she tries to palm a few off.

Mum holds the box while Uncle Simon chooses. He points at one and says, *What's this one?*

I don't know, Si.

This one?

I don't know, Si.

And this one?

I don't know, Si, there's no menu card so you just have to guess.

Does this one have nuts in?

Listen Si, I think Mandy needs to rest up, so maybe come back tomorrow, yeah. You can take the whole box with you if you like.

Uncle Simon gets up to go, *Hhhhmm jacket on or off?*

Mum whispers 'fuckin' ell' really quietly to herself.

7pm
I go up to Josh's room with a box of Grandad's chocolates. Auntie Mandy's in bed with all her candles on, half watching a documentary on Channel 5 about naked neighbours and half reading a book called *I Killed For The One... Again*. We try and find the nice chocolates by biting a bit off each one, and I talk about the time I thought I saw Carol next door gardening naked but she was just wearing beige trousers.

GIRL POWER

4pm

I've got an hour to find a fancy dress outfit in Nanny Pam's wardrobe!

Sammy is having a fancy dress party tonight in the church hall. At break time today, she asked if I wanted to go because Natalie's got diarrhoea and can't go anymore, so her mum said she had to ask someone else because she's paid for thirty.

Everyone in my class, apart from me and Alan, got an invitation last week. Then even Alan got invited a few days ago because his mum kicked off at Sammy's mum in the playground.

I only said yes to going because Tom's going to be there and Amy's going too. Amy got invited because her mum works with Sammy's mum at the doctors surgery. She didn't want to go but her mum's making her and even bought her a proper Baby Spice outfit for it.

We go for tea round Nanny Pam's on Thursday nights, because Mum's at college, and Dad's got a new job. Usually we just sit around and eat stuff out of Nanny Pam's freezer while we watch all the soaps. I won't even get to watch Neighbours tonight though, because I need to sort my costume out!

Jenny and Josh are sat in the living room watching Round The Twist and getting stuck into a box of choc-ices. From the kitchen I can hear them singing the wrong words to the theme tune but I'm not in the mood to argue with Jenny.

Auntie Maeve's round at Nanny Pam's too. Usually I like seeing Maeve, she tells funny stories. Once she said she saw Chris Akabusi in Marks and Spencer's buying his underpants, and another time she said she won a conservatory in The Daily Mail, but they wouldn't give it to her because she lives in a top floor flat. I don't have time to listen to her tonight though. Luckily she's too busy reading one of Nanny Pam's *Take A Break* magazines out loud to herself.

I had sex with a ghost!..he was wearin' nothin' but a Jacobean ruff...might have been Shakespeare...it felt dead cold like a Callipo!

I start panicking about the party and my costume to Nanny Pam. She takes some overdone fish fingers out from under the grill and says, *Look love, if you could go as anyone who would it be?*

I think for a bit. I'd like to go as Jet from Gladiators, but I'm not wearing Nanny Pam's swimming costume and I think that all the other girls will be going as Spice Girls, so I probably should as well.

4.30pm

I eat my fish finger sandwich faster than ever, and go upstairs with Nanny Pam to find an outfit.

Nanny Pam says, *Right, well my joggers are in the wash after bums and tums, so I can't do you a Sporty Spice. I sold my blonde wig at a boot sale last week so that rules out Baby, I don't like that miserable Posh one, and I'm not getting a bollocking for dressing you up as that slapper Ginger. What about Scary Spice? I've got some leopard print in here somewhere...*

4.40pm

Nanny Pam finds me some black leggings to wear with a silky leopard print blouse. All of Nanny Pam's shoes are too small for me so I put my school shoes back on.

Nanny Pam starts crimping my hair, and Maeve comes upstairs to help with my make-up. I look up at the pink streaks across Maeve's cheeks and the sparkly blue circles around her eyes and start worrying again.

When they're both finished I stand up on Nanny Pam's bed and look in the big mirror on her dressing table. I look like Nanny Pam Spice.

5.30pm

I'm late for the party because we had to drop Maeve off on the way.

When Nanny Pam says goodbye to someone it usually means it will be at least another hour before they actually leave, especially if it's Maeve! And just as she was getting out of the car she started telling Nanny Pam a massive story about the time her friend found a dead mouse in a Wispa, and that she always chops them up before she eats them now.

I walk into the church hall and through all the Spice Girls I can see Tom in the corner with Matt near Sammy's dad, who's dressed in a really tight Elvis costume. Tom's dressed as Liam Gallagher. He's drawn sideburns on his face with black felt-tip and has a long green parka on. My tummy flips and I go to find Amy.

Amy's sat down with Alan by the buffet putting Hula Hoops on her fingers. Alan's still in his school uniform and is stacking up party rings on the table. I grab a handful of skips and sit down next to them. We watch all the other Spice Girls for a bit. Sammy's dressed as Posh and Rachel's dressed as Ginger. They keep running up to the boys and saying stuff then running back to the rest of the girls to giggle.

5.40pm
Sammy comes over to me and Amy, and we shuffle up to let her sit down. The other girls are acting really daft across the room, whispering and giggling. Sammy says to me, *Tom wants to know if you'll go out with him.*

I feel really shaky and hot. I look at Amy, she smiles and bites a Hula Hoop off her finger.

Sammy stands up and pulls me up with her, then pushes me towards Tom.

5.45pm

I wipe my Skips fingers on Nanny Pam's leggings and smooth my hair, which has gone really frizzy from all the crimping.

I walk up to Tom and say hi. He nods at me and then carries on talking to Matt I stand next to him and Matt for a bit without saying anything. I look across the room. Amy's watching me and looking nervous, Alan's karate chopping stacks of Party Rings, Sammy's dad's pulling his Elvis trousers out of his bum crack and eating sausage rolls, and all the other Spice Girls are laughing their heads off in the corner near the door.

Tom shouts to the girls, *What are youse lot laughing at?*

Sammy shouts back, *Holly thinks you're going out with her!*

Tom looks at me and I look at my school shoes, then he looks back at the girls.

Sammy shouts, *As if you'd go out with her, right?*

Tom looks at me again then back at Sammy and eventually says quietly, *Yeah as if.*

5.50pm
I run out of the hall crying my head off with Baby Amy Spice following me.

Outside, I cry some more but also start feeling angry and start to kick a bin for a bit. Amy asks if we should go back in the hall and ring her mum to pick us up early. I tell her that there's no way we're going back in there, and that we'll just have to wait in the car park until her mum comes at seven.

6pm
I finally stop crying, and me and Amy decide to walk to Londis down the road and come back at seven so we don't have to see anyone or hear the stupid music coming from the hall.

6.10pm
Tasha is smoking outside Londis with all her gothy mates. I tell Amy that we're going to have to go back to the car park because the last thing I need is Tasha taking the piss as well.

We turn around and start walking back to the Church Hall, but it's too late. Tasha shouts, *HOLLLLLLLEEEEEEE!*

Tasha's drunk. She runs up to me, gives me a big fat hug and tells me that she loves me. Her coat smells like a hamster's wee corner and fags. When she eventually lets go she looks at me and asks, *Have you been crying? Why are you dressed like a twat?*

Baby Amy Spice tells Tasha everything and I start crying again.

6.20pm
We hang out with Tasha and her mates for a bit, they drink cider and smoke loads of fags, and me and Amy share a Bounty.

6.45pm
Tasha and her mates walk us back to the car park. Everyone from the party is stood outside waiting for their parents to pick them up. Sammy's with them saying goodbye, when she sees me she starts laughing again with the other girls.

Tasha looks over at them and shouts, *Shut the fuck up you tragic little slags!* All of Tasha's mates start shouting too, one even says the C word! All the Spice Girls stop laughing, and Sammy starts crying. Sammy's dad comes out and tells the Goths to piss off but they just start laughing and Tasha says something about seeing Elvis's ball sack.

6.50pm
Amy's Mum pulls up and we jump in the car. Through the

back window I watch the Goths shouting at Elvis and the Spice Girls. Then I notice Liam Gallagher looking straight at me. I look back at him. The car engine starts. He's still looking at me and I think he smiles. The car pulls away. I stick my middle finger up.